# Greatest Hits



Exclusive distributors:
Music Sales Limited
8/9 Frith Street,
London W1V 5TZ, England.
Music Sales Pty Limited
120 Rothschild Avenue
Rosebery, NSW 2018,
Australia.

Order No.AM962676
ISBN 0-7119-8033-0


Printed in the United Kingdom by
Printwise (Haverhill) Limited, Suffolk



Wise Publications
London/New York/Sydney/Paris/Copenhagen/Madrid/Tokyo

£8.00
2/00

# Come On Over

Words & Music by Shania Twain & R.J. Lange

E
A
get a grip,
get a - way some - where, take a trip.
E
Take a break,
take con - trol,
take ad - vice
A
E
from some - one you know.
Come on o - ver,
A
come on in;
pull up a seat,
take a load off your feet.

E
A
Come on o - ver, come on in; you can un - wind, take a
load off your mind. Make a wish, make a move, make up
F
your mind, you can choose. When you're up, when you're down,
B♭
F
when you need a laugh, come a - round.
B♭

F
B♭
Come on o - ver, come on in; pull up a seat, take a
F
load off your feet. Come on o - ver, come on in;
B♭
F
you can un - wind, take a load off your mind. Oh,
B♭
oh.

F
B♭
Oh, oh.
F♯
Be a win - ner, be a star, yeah, be hap -
get a grip, get a - way
B
- py to be who you are. Got - ta be
some - where, take a trip. Take a break,
F♯
your - self, got - ta make a plan, got - ta go
take con - trol, take ad - vice

B
F♯
for it while you can, yeah.
from some - one you know.
Come on o - ver,
B
come on in;
pull up a seat, take a load off your feet.
F♯
B
To Coda
Come on o - ver, come on in;
you can un - wind, take a
F♯
load off your mind.

B
F♯
B
D.S. al Coda
Get a life,
CODA
B
F♯
load off your mind, yeah.
Come on o -
B
- ver, come on in.
Yeah, come on, come on.

F♯
B
Oh, ___
oh. ___
N.C.
Oh, ___
B
F♯
oh. ___
Oh, ___
B
N.C.
oh, ___
come _ on in.

# Any Man Of Mine

Words & Music by Shania Twain & R.J. Lange

still bet - ter love me. And I can be late for a date, that's fine, but he
bet - ter be on time.
Ab5
4fr
N.C.
And an - y man of mine 'll say it
an - y man of mine bet - ter
Ab5
4fr
N.C.
Eb5
N.C.
Ab5
4fr
N.C.
fits just right when last year's dress is just a lit - tle too tight. And an - y -
dis - a - gree when I say an - oth - er wom - an's look - in' bet - ter than me. And
Ab5
4fr
N.C.
Ab5
4fr
N.C.
Eb5
N.C.
thing I do or say bet - ter be o - kay when I have a bad hair day.
when I cook him din - ner and I burn it black, he bet - ter say, "Mmmm, I

Ab5
N.C.
C5
Db5
N.C.
G5
Ab5
N.C.
like it like _ that." Yeah!
And if I change my mind _ a
C5
Db5
N.C.
Eb5
N.C.
mil - lion _ times, _
I wan-na hear him say, _ "Yeah, _ (yeah,)
Eb5
N.C.
Eb5
N.C.
Eb5
N.C.
yeah, _ (yeah,) yeah, I like it that _ way!" _
An - y man _ of
Country two-beat
Db
Ab
Eb
mine bet-ter walk the line. _
Bet-ter show me a teas - in', squeez-in',

Ab
4 fr
Db
pleas - in' kind of time.
I need a man who knows
Ab
4 fr
Gb
how the sto - ry goes.
He's got - ta be a heart - beat - in', fine treat - in',
Db
Eb
3 fr
1
N.C.
breath - tak - in', earth - quak - in' kind,
an - y man of
Ab5
4 fr
N.C.
Ab5
4 fr
N.C.
Eb5
N.C.
Ab5
4 fr
N.C.
mine.
Well,

2
N.C.
D♭
A♭
4fr
an - y man of mine.
(Instrumental solo)
D♭
(Solo ends) Let me hear you say,
E♭
3fr
E♭7
"Yeah, (yeah,) yeah, (yeah,) yeah, I like it that way!"
A♭
4fr
N.C.
B♭
N.C.
An - y man, an - y man, an - y man...
An - y man of

E♭
B♭
mine
bet - ter walk the line.
F
B♭
Bet - ter show me a teas - in', squeez - in', pleas - in' kind of time.
E♭
B♭
I need a man who knows how the sto - ry goes.
A♭
E♭
He's got - ta be a heart - beat - in', fine treat - in', breath - tak - in', earth - quak - in'

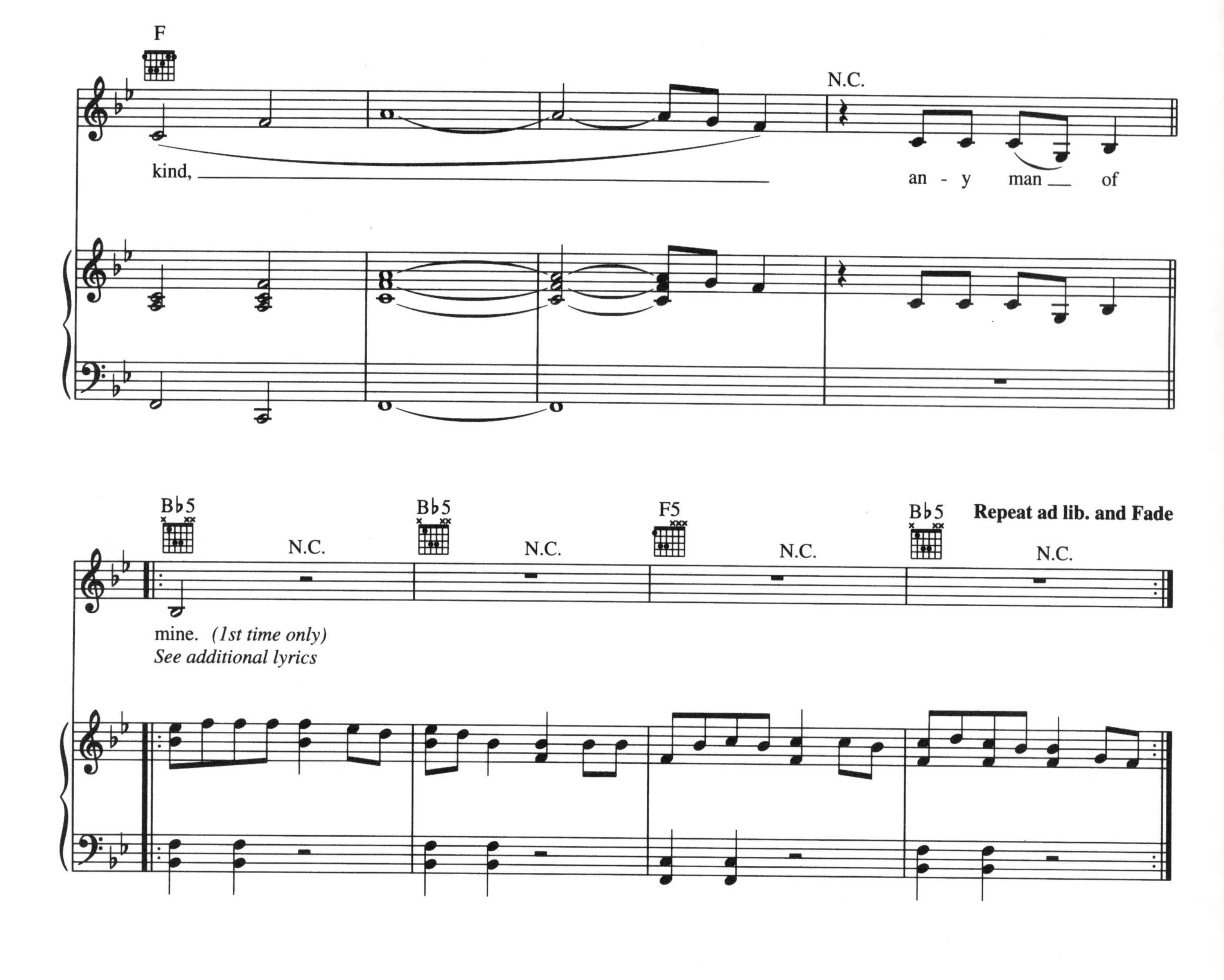

*Additional Lyrics*

*(Spoken:)* You gotta shimmy, shake, make the earth quake.
Kick, turn, stomp, stomp, then you jump heel to toe. Do-si-do
'Til your boots wanna break, 'til your feet and your back ache.
Keep it movin' 'til you just can't take anymore.
Come on, everybody on the floor, a-one two, a-three four.
Hup two, hup if you wanna be a man of mine, that's right.
This is what a woman wants...

# Don't Be Stupid (You Know I Love You)

Words & Music by Shania Twain & R.J. Lange

don't ap - pre - ci - ate it. When I talk to oth - er guys, you think they're
on my tail. I
get so ag - gra - vat - ed when I get off the phone and get the
Stop o - ver - re - act - ing. You e - ven get sus - pi - cious when I
third de - gree. I'm real - ly feel - in' frus - trat - ed. Why don't you
paint my nails. It's def - i - nite - ly dis - tract - ing the way you

G5
D
take a pill and put a lit - tle trust in me? And you'll see.
dram - a - tize ev - 'ry lit - tle small de - tail.
N.C.
D
G5
D
A
Don't freak out un - til you know the facts. Re - lax.
Don't freak out un - til you know the facts. Re - lax, Max.
Don't be
D
G5
D
A
D
G5
(1.,2.) stu - pid, you know I love you. Don't be ri - dic - u - lous, you know I
(D.S.) you. Instrumental
D
A
D
G5
D
A
need you. Don't be ab - surd, you know I want you. Don't be im -

D
G5
3 fr
A
Bm
pos - si - ble.
Instrumental ends
I'm mad a - bout
G/B
you.
Can't live with - out you.
Em/B
To Coda
I'm cra - zy 'bout you.
Don't be stu - pid, you know
1
I love you.

D
A
D.S. al Coda
I love
CODA
you. Don't be stu-pid, you know I love you. Don't be ri-
2. Vocal ad lib.
G5
3fr
dic-u-lous, you know I need you. Don't be ab-surd, you know I want you. Don't be im-
pos-si-ble, im-pos-si-ble. ble. Don't be stu-pid.

# Man! I Feel Like A Woman!

Words & Music by Shania Twain & R.J. Lange

E♭5
B♭5
fr6
3
- na let it all hang out.
Wan - na make some noise, real -
- ly raise my voice.
Yeah, I wan - na scream and shout.
1.
2, 3.
N.C.
Ah!
2. No
A♭
fr4
B♭
The best thing a - bout be - ing a wo - man is the pre - ro - ga - tive to

3º only
N.C.
F
have a lit-tle fun and... Fun, fun! Oh, oh, oh
3
go to-tal-ly cra - zy, for-get I'm a la - dy, men's shirts, short
Dm
B♭
skirts, oh, oh, oh real-ly go wild, yeah, do - in' it in
style. Oh, oh, oh, get in the ac - tion, feel the at-trac - tion.

Dm7
Co-lour my hair, do what I dare. Oh, oh, oh, I wan-na be free, yeah to
B♭
To Coda
Gm7
fr3
1.
N.C.
feel the way I feel. Man! I feel like a
B♭5
wo - man.
E♭5
fr6
3. The girls

2.
N.C.
Man! I feel like a wo-man.
B♭5
E♭5
fr6
B♭5
A♭5
fr4
E♭5
fr6
B♭5
D.%. al Coda
Coda
feel
(Feel the way I feel.) Man! I feel like a

*Verse 2:*
No inhibitions
Make no conditions
Get a little outta line
I ain't gonna act
Politically correct
I only wanna have a good time

The best thing *etc.*

*Verse 3:*
The girls need a break
Tonight we're gonna take
The chance to get out on the town.
We don't need romance
We only wanna dance
We're gonna let our hair hang down.

The best thing *etc.*

# From This Moment On

Words & Music by Shania Twain & R.J. Lange

Cadd9
G
Am7
D add11
fr5
you is where I be - long
from this mo - ment on.
From this mo - ment I have been blessed, I live
D
Con pedale
on - ly for your hap - pi - ness. And for your
love I'd give my last breath,

Am7
D
Cadd9
from this mo - ment on.
I give
G
C
my hand to you with all my heart,
I can't
D/F♯
G
wait to live my life with you, I can't wait to start.
Cadd9
Em7
You and I will ne - ver be a - part,
my dreams came true

Cmaj9
G
G/D
D
because of you. From this
C
G
D
A
E
moment, as long as I live, I will
A
E
Dadd9
E
Dadd9
A
love you, I promise you this. There is nothing I wouldn't give
D
E
B E
D
A
Bm7
E
Dadd9
from this moment on. Uh-huh!
A
B
F♯ E
D

A
F♯m7
Guitar solo
Dadd9
fr2
E
A
D
You're the rea - son I be - lieve in love and
E
A
you're the an - swer to my prayers from up a - bove.

Dadd9
fr2
All we need is just the two of us, my dreams
F♯m7
Dmaj9
fr4
A
came true because of you
E
N.C.
From this
B
F♯
Eadd9
mo - ment, as long as I live I will love you, I

F♯
Eadd9
B
promise you this. There is nothing I wouldn't give
C♯m7
F♯
from this moment. I will love
Eadd9
B
C♯m7
F♯
you as long as I live from this moment
Eadd9
B/D♯
F♯sus4
B
rit.
on. Mm mm mm.
8vb

# That Don't Impress Me Much

Words & Music by Shania Twain & R.J. Lange

you've got be - ing right down to an art. You think you're a gen - ius, you drive me
up the wall. You're a re - gu - lar o - ri - gi - nal know - it - all.
A♭
fr4
E♭ B♭ A♭ B♭ E♭ B♭
fr3 fr4 fr3
Ooh, ooh you think you're spe - cial. Ooh, ooh you think you're
A♭
fr4
N.C.
some-thing else. O. K. So you're a rock-et sci-en-tist. That don't im -
Drums

G♭ D♭ A♭ B♭m G♭ D♭ A♭
-press me much. (Uh uh ooh) So you got the brains but have you
2° (looks)
B♭m
got the touch? Now don't get me wrong, yeah I think you're al - right. But
N.C.
that won't keep me warm in the mid - dle of the night.
Drums
1. B♭m G♭
2. B♭m G♭maj7
That don't im - press me much. (Uh much.

A♭
B♭m
G♭maj7
fr4
Uh ow!
Yeah.
Ooh!
You're
N.C.
one of those guys who likes to shine his ma - chine, you make me
Drums
take off my shoes be - fore you let me get in.
I can't be - lieve you kiss your
G♭

A♭
B♭m
G♭
A♭
car good-night, now come on ba-by tell me, you must be jo-kin' right?
E♭
B♭
A♭
B♭
E♭
B♭
Ooh, ooh you think you're some-thing spe-cial. Ooh, ooh you think you're
A♭
N.C.
some-thing else. O. K. so you got a car. That don't im-
G♭
D♭
A♭
B♭m
G♭
D♭
A♭
-press me much. (Uh uh ooh) So you got the moves but have you
2° (You think you're cool)

G♭
D♭
A♭
B♭m
fr4
got the touch?
Now don't get me wrong, yeah I think you're al - right? But
that won't keep me warm in the mid - dle of the night. That don't im -
2° (on the long
1.
2.
N.C.
cold lone - ly nights.
Drums
B♭sus4 2
That don't im - press me much. (Uh uh uh) Uh huh

*Verse 2:*
I never knew a guy who carried a mirror in his pocket
And a comb up his sleeve; just in case
And all that extra-hold gel in your hair oughta lock it
'Cause Heaven forbid it should fall outta place.

Ooh, ooh you think you're special
Ooh, ooh you think you're something else
Okay, so you're Brad Pitt.

That don't impress me much *etc.*

# You're Still The One

Words & Music by Shania Twain & R.J. Lange

A♭
B♭
E♭
we knew we'd get there some - day. They said,
E♭/G
A♭
B♭
I bet, they'll nev - er make it, but just
E♭
A♭
B♭
look at us hold - ing on, we're still to - geth-
E♭
A♭
B♭
A♭
- er, still go - ing strong. (Still the one.)

E♭
fr3
A♭
fr4
Fm7
You're still the one I run to the one that I be - long
B♭
E♭
A♭
to. You're still the one I want for
life. (Still the one.) You're still the one that I love,
the on - ly one I dream of, you're still the one I kiss

*Verse 2:*
Ain't nothing better
We beat the odds together
I'm glad we didn't listen
Look at what we would be missing.

They said, I bet,
They'll never make it
But just look at us holding on
We're still together, still going strong.

# The Woman In Me (Needs The Man In You)

Words & Music by Shania Twain & R.J. Lange

Eb(add2)
Gm7
F
Dm7
be the rock that you see,
much, and it feels cold and out of touch,
Bb
Cm
Bb/D
when the nights get too long and I just can't go on.
it's a beau - ti - ful place when you kiss my face.
The wom - an in
Eb
Ebsus
Eb/G
me needs you to be
Dm/A
Gm
the man in my arms to hold ten - der - ly.

B♭ F B♭ E♭
'Cause I'm a wom - an in love,
and it's you I run
Gm Cm7 E♭
to.
Yeah, the wom - an in me
1
F
needs the man in
B♭(add9) Dm7 F
you.
When the world wants too
2
F
needs the man in you.
a tempo
Repeat and Fade
Optional Ending
B♭(add9) Dm7 E♭(add2) F B♭(add9) Dm7 E♭(add2) F
B♭(add9)